The Shark Who Was Afraid of Everything!

by Brian James

Illustrated by Bruce McNally

Cartwheel
B·O·O·K·S

SCHOLASTIC INC.

New York   Toronto   London   Auckland   Sydney
Mexico City   New Delhi   Hong Kong   Buenos Aires

Sharkie the Shark was unlike all the others.
Sharkie was teased by his sisters and brothers.

Under the sea, where they all played,
Sharkie the Shark was always afraid.

He was afraid of whales with great, big tails.

He was scared of ships with little sails.

Sharkie feared the silly seals.

He swam away from electric eels.

No other sharks would let Sharkie play.

"Fraidy Shark! Fraidy Shark!"
is what they would say.

Sharkie was afraid of the dark.
He was afraid of the light.

But he was most afraid
the other sharks might be right!

"What good is a shark who's always scared?

I'll go far away where no one will care!"

Lily the Little Fish watched Sharkie leave.
Lily the Little Fish followed his lead.

Sharkie was happy to have a new friend.
Together they played and loved to pretend.

They made silly faces, swam upside-down races,

had hide-and-seek chases in all kinds of places.

But after awhile, they needed to rest.
"I think that we're lost," Sharkie confessed.

"Sharkie, I'm scared!" Lily then cried.
"I'm not. It's okay," Sharkie replied.

Sharkie knew he had to save the day.

It was up to him to lead the way.

He took Lily by the hand.

This way and that way, together they swam.

Soon they were home. Everyone was there!

"Where were you two? We were so scared!"

Lily smiled and Sharkie did, too.

Everyone nodded and shook their head.

Then Sharkie the Shark stood proud and tall
'cause everyone said he was the bravest of all!

The Shark Who Was Afraid of Everything!

To my Little Tiger for teaching me to be brave.
—B.J.

To the memory of Ellen and Jimmy.
—B.M.

ISBN 0-439-78672-X

Text copyright © 2002 by Brian James.
Illustrations copyright © 2002 by Bruce McNally.
All rights reserved. Published by Scholastic Inc.

SCHOLASTIC, CARTWHEEL BOOKS, and associated logos are trademarks and/or registered trademarks of Scholastic Inc.

12 11 10 9 8 7 6 5 4 3 2   6 7 8 9 10 11 /0
Printed in the U.S.A. 40
First printing, May 2006